Smoking stinks!!

Written by Kim Gosselin

Illustrated by Thom Buttner

SCHOLASTIC INC.

New York   Toronto   London   Auckland   Sydney
Mexico City   New Delhi   Hong Kong

ISBN 0-590-52244-2

12 11 10 9 8 7 6 5 4 3 2 1   8 9/9 0 1 2 3/0

Printed in the U.S.A.   14

First Scholastic printing, November 1998

Edited by Barbara A. Mitchell
Design by Carol Stanton

Here's What Professionals Are Saying About <u>Smoking STINKS!!</u>

Heartwarming and Educational!!

"Cigarette smoking is the single most important risk factor for lung and heart disease. Keeping children from starting to smoke is the most important thing that society can do to improve everyone's health. **Smoking STINKS!!** presents important information clearly and in a way that children can easily understand. Kim Gosselin's book is an excellent contribution to education of all children about this very important health concern."

— ROBERT C. STRUNK, M.D.
Director, Division of Allergy & Pulmonary Medicine
Washington University School of Medicine
Saint Louis, Missouri

An Investment in Children's Health!

"As an elementary school teacher, I strongly urge parents to invest in their children's future health by having them read **Smoking STINKS!!** The book is fun to read and provides a clear message to all young readers. The warm relationships between the characters feel real and will most certainly give more weight to the message of the dangers of smoking. I plan on incorporating this book into my curriculum as soon as possible!"

— AMY L. JOHNSON
Elementary School Teacher

Great Education for Kids!

"**Smoking STINKS!!** gets the message about the harmful and unpleasant effects of smoking across in a way that is clearly portrayed and appealing to children and students. Good educational practice relates learning to students' life experiences. Kim Gosselin's book does so in a convincing and eminently appealing fashion. If we can ingrain the message in students' minds during elementary and middle school, they will be much better equipped to resist the temptation to smoke later in life."

— MICHAEL CERUTTI, PRINCIPAL
Wren Hollow Elementary School

Excellent Ammunition for the War on Tobacco

"As a member of an anti-tobacco coalition that focuses on education and advocacy for young people, I am thrilled with **Smoking STINKS!!** It fills a gap which exists in tobacco education on our library and bookstore shelves. Fiction filled with facts is a powerful tool in reaching school children. The anti-tobacco war continues with fresh supplies — thanks, Kim Gosselin."

— KRISTA V. SCHAAFSMA MT(ASCP)
Nico-Team Consultant (funded by ASSIST)
Butterworth Hospital and American Lung Association
Grand Rapids, Michigan

Well Done!! A "Must Have"!!

"Cigarette smoking is an important child health concern. **Smoking STINKS!!** is a wonderfully crafted illustration of how significant this issue is for children with allergies and asthma. Congratulations to Kim Gosselin on creating another remarkable work of art, which educates children on the need for avoiding cigarette smoke, while imparting the critical message to never begin smoking. This first book in the 'Substance Free Kids' series gives children and families courage and support to understand and talk about difficult issues."

— PHILLIP E. KORENBLAT, M.D.
Professor of Clinical Medicine, Washington University School of Medicine
Medical Director of The Asthma Center and Director of Clinical Research
at Barnes-Jewish West County Hospital
Saint Louis, Missouri

A True Winner!

"Cigarette smoke is harmful to the smoker and to those around them. Kim Gosselin has produced a wonderful educational book to assist children in learning about this health problem. As in her other well-illustrated books, she presents the information in a manner that children can understand. The message is clear: '**Smoking STINKS!!**'"

— GARY S. RACHELEFSKY, M.D.
Clinical Professor, Pediatrics
University of California at Los Angeles
Director, Allergy Research Foundation, Inc.

Bravo! It's About Time.

"**Smoking STINKS!!** is a necessary teaching tool for children without the lecturing that sometimes goes along with teaching. We should have more wonderful methods like this for our kids."

— MELBA R. MOORE
Director, Tobacco Use-Prevention and Control
American Lung Association Eastern Missouri

Acknowledgements

I wish to thank the American Lung Association and the American Cancer Society for their support of my work which is dedicated to the enjoyment and education of all children, particularly those living with chronic health conditions.

I also wish to extend my sincere appreciation to the many physicians and health professionals who took time out of their extremely busy schedules to review <u>Smoking STINKS!!</u>

—Kim Gosselin

A Note from the Author

As a child I was blessed with three loving grandfathers. The memories of my time spent with them are dear to my heart, and I shall treasure them always.

Grandpa "K" delighted in taking me to my first amusement park where I rode the carousel in awe. Grandpa "G" squeezed me tight with loving "bear hugs" and slipped me a dollar whenever he came visiting. "Little" Grandpa lived with me, and was a treasured part of the family (all seventy pounds of him). As I grew older, he convincingly praised my canned spaghetti dinners, and played soulful songs on his harmonica before climbing into bed each night.

Grandpa "K" smoked cigars and tobacco in a pipe. He died from lung cancer.

Grandpa "G" smoked cigarettes. He died from smoking-related heart disease.

"Little" Grandpa chewed tobacco and smoked cigarettes. He passed away from lung cancer and emphysema.

Smoking STINKS.

Dedicated in loving memory to
Grandpa K., Grandpa G., and Little Grandpa
and to Mother, with all my love.

The bell rang just as Maddie shoved her
books into her cubbie and plopped down in her seat.
Her friend Alex read the day's announcements.
Maddie didn't seem to hear a word.

Mr. Jenkins handed out the class's special assignment reminder. Their health reports were due by Friday. Maddie hadn't even started! She was too worried about her Grandpa Norman. Grandpa Norman had a bad cough. His cough seemed to be getting worse lately. The awful hacking noise coming from Grandpa Norman's bedroom woke Maddie up nearly every night now.

On top of everything else, Maddie's allergies were bugging her again. Grandpa Norman's cigarette smoking always seemed to make her allergies worse! Maddie grabbed a tissue from the space under her desk and wiped her dribbling nose. **"SMOKING STINKS!!"** she shouted aloud.

Maddie looked up sheepishly.
Fifty-two enormous round eyes,
in various shades of brown, blue, and green,
stared straight through her!

"Health report?" Maddie's heart pounded fiercely. "Oh, yeah!" she bounced back. "My health report's going to be um.... about smoking."

"Great topic!" said Mr. Jenkins. "I'm sure the whole class would agree with you, that smoking, indeed, STINKS!"

The giggles subsided as Maddie sank deeper and deeper into her chair. She couldn't wait until the school day was over; and yet, it had only just begun.

Later, Maddie tried to concentrate on her new spelling words. She doodled clouds of smoke in the margins of her notebook paper, and wrapped a loose curl around her forefinger. Finally, it was time for lunch. Maddie grabbed her lunch bag and headed towards the cafeteria. Her friend, Alex, caught up with her, just as the rest of the class rounded the hall corner.

"Hey, Maddie! My health report's on smoking too," he announced.

"Let's ask Mr. Jenkins if we can work together."

"Are you sure you wouldn't be too embarrassed?" she asked, accusingly.

"Naw," he replied, tearing into his bag of chips.

"Besides, smoking does STINK....in more ways than one."

"What do you mean?" she asked, sitting down next to him.

"Well, my mom smokes too," Alex said, munching on a potato chip. "Our whole house stinks like a chimney. Plus, I've got asthma. Breathing in somebody else's smoke usually makes it even worse!"

"Yeah, it bothers my allergies too," Maddie said. "SMOKING STINKS!!" she said again, while taking a big bite out of the apple from her lunch bag.

After lunch, Maddie and Alex talked to Mr. Jenkins about working together on their health report. Mr. Jenkins thought it was a great idea! He even suggested they find a guest speaker to come in and talk to the class with them.

That night, Alex and Maddie worked on their health report at Grandpa Norman and Maddie's kitchen table. They asked Grandpa Norman a million questions about smoking. Maddie and Alex took turns scribbling down notes in their spiral binders while listening to Grandpa Norman speak.

"Why did you ever start smoking?" asked Alex. "Because I thought it was cool," he answered, disgusted with his dirty ashtray sitting on the table. "I was about fifteen at the time. All my friends were smoking, and I just wanted to be like them."

"Why don't you quit?" asked Maddie, simply.

"Oh, Maddie," Grandpa said, "I've tried so many times. You see, it's not so easy to quit. Smoking is an addiction because tobacco has nicotine in it."

Maddie gulped. "What's NICOTINE?"

Grandpa Norman stared at Maddie and Alex hard. He looked straight into their eyes, hesitating only to stop and catch his breath. "Nicotine is poison!" he said, lightly pounding his fist on the kitchen table. "It's a very powerful DRUG!!"

"Wow," gasped Alex. "A drug! No wonder my mom said smoking cigarettes was a lot like taking drugs. She told me her brain knows smoking's bad for her, but her body feels like she really NEEDS it."

"That's exactly right!" Grandpa Norman said, struggling to get up and out of his chair. "An addiction means that it's hard to stop. And it doesn't matter if you smoke cigars, a pipe, cigarettes, or use chewing or 'spit' tobacco— the addiction is the same. The smartest thing you kids can do is to NEVER start!!"

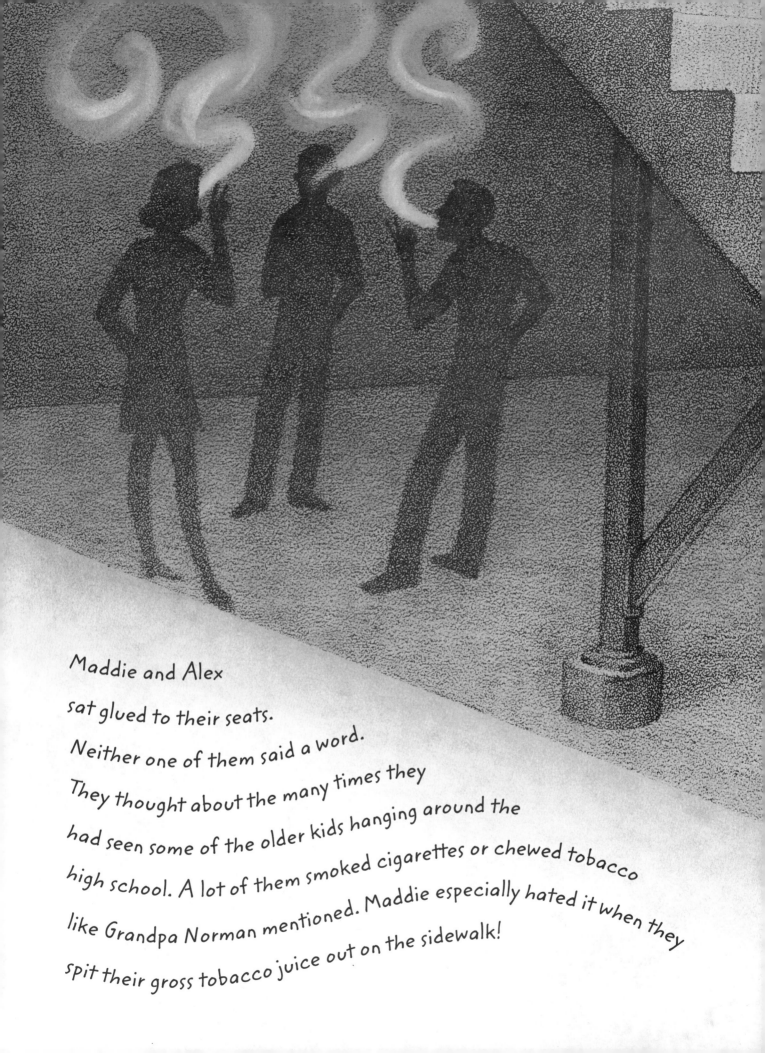

Maddie and Alex
sat glued to their seats.
Neither one of them said a word.
They thought about the many times they
had seen some of the older kids hanging around the
high school. A lot of them smoked cigarettes or chewed tobacco
like Grandpa Norman mentioned. Maddie especially hated it when they
spit their gross tobacco juice out on the sidewalk!

Grandpa Norman went on to tell Maddie and Alex about the many different diseases smoking could cause. He rattled off words Maddie and Alex could hardly even say. Words like BRONCHITIS and EMPHYSEMA. And then, of course, he reminded them about things they already knew about. Things like HEART DISEASE and CANCER.

Maddie had heard the word EMPHYSEMA before. She heard Grandpa Norman talking to Doctor Parkin about it on the phone. She wondered if emphysema was what made Grandpa Norman cough so much. Did emphysema make it hard for him to even breathe?

Later, after Alex had gone home, Grandpa Norman tucked Maddie into bed. She saw the ugly brown stains on his fingers from the tobacco in his cigarettes, and smelled the smoke in his favorite flannel nightshirt. Maddie understood things better now. She understood that Grandpa Norman was probably addicted to nicotine. Even so, she loved him with all her heart!

Maddie asked Grandpa Norman if he would be a guest speaker for her health report on Friday. He said he'd be glad to, especially if he could help stop kids from making some of the same mistakes that he had! He even promised to ask Doctor Parkin to come along. Dr. Parkin could be a guest speaker too!

The rest of the week, Maddie and Alex worked hard at school on their health report. Doctor Parkin let them borrow a giant poster. It showed a picture of two lungs. One of them was healthy and pink (the way lungs should be). But the other lung was brown and sick-looking (from smoking). "Smoking STINKS!!" thought Maddie and Alex, as they hung the poster up on the classroom wall.

Finally it was Friday! Maddie and Alex shared their health report on smoking with Mr. Jenkins and the whole class. Doctor Parkin stood in the front of the room and told the kids how smoking caused many, many people to get very sick. "A lot of people get sick and even die EVERY DAY from smoking-related diseases," Dr. Parkin said, sadly.

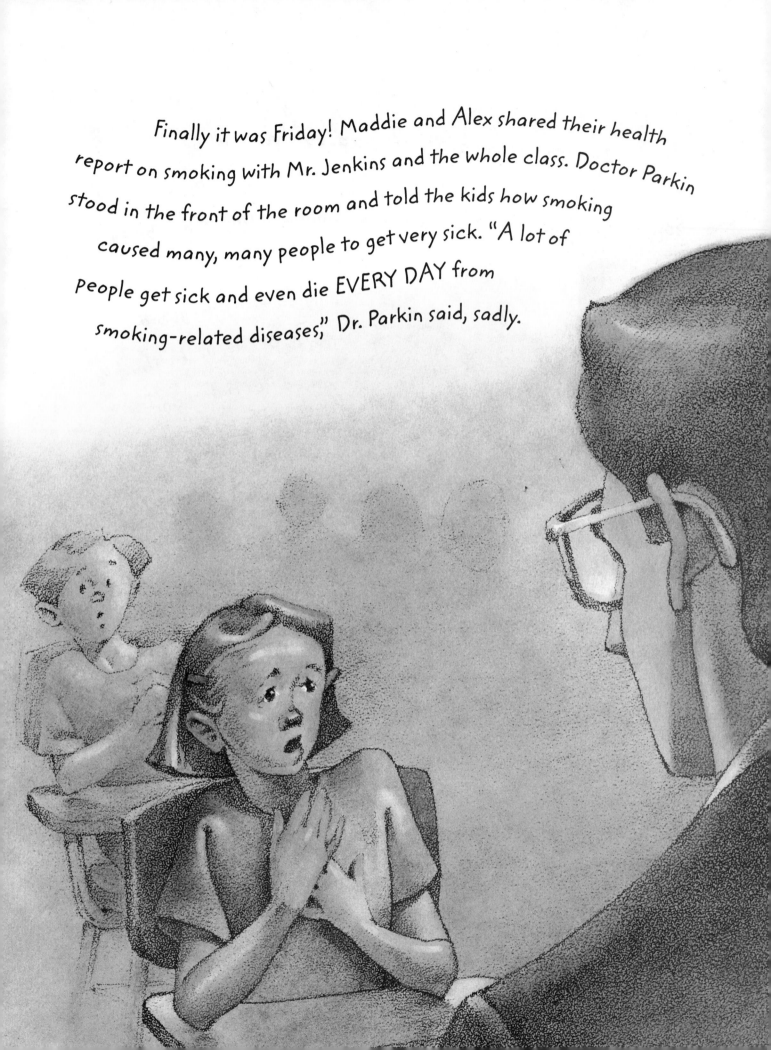

Next, Dr. Parkin talked about "passive" or "secondhand" smoke (breathing in the smoke of someone's burning cigar or cigarette). He said secondhand smoke was bad for ANYBODY to breathe. But it could be much worse for kids who were living with allergies or asthma. Gertie, in the third row, raised her right hand.

"I have asthma," she said. "You mean, if I breathe in somebody else's smoke, my asthma might get worse?" "That's possible," answered Dr. Parkin, while Alex and Maddie nodded in agreement. "Smoke of any kind can help trigger an asthma episode."

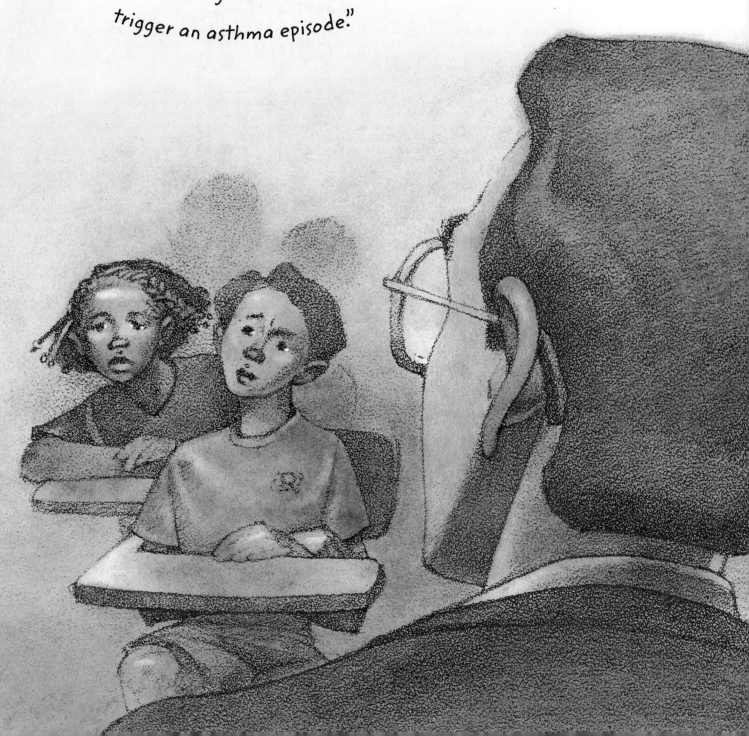

"What about 'spit' tobacco?" asked the tall skinny kid with glasses. "I see a lot of baseball players using it, so it must be safe, right?"

"WRONG!" answered Dr. Parkin, firmly. "Chewing or 'spit' tobacco can lead to many of the same problems other tobacco causes, or even start new ones! Just remember kids, there is NO SAFE TOBACCO!!!"

Next it was Grandpa Norman's turn to speak.

First, he did something the kids thought was pretty weird.

Grandpa Norman passed around his favorite flannel

night shirt for all of them to SMELL!

"GROSS!!" said Gertie, taking in a big whiff.

"Smoking STINKS!!!"

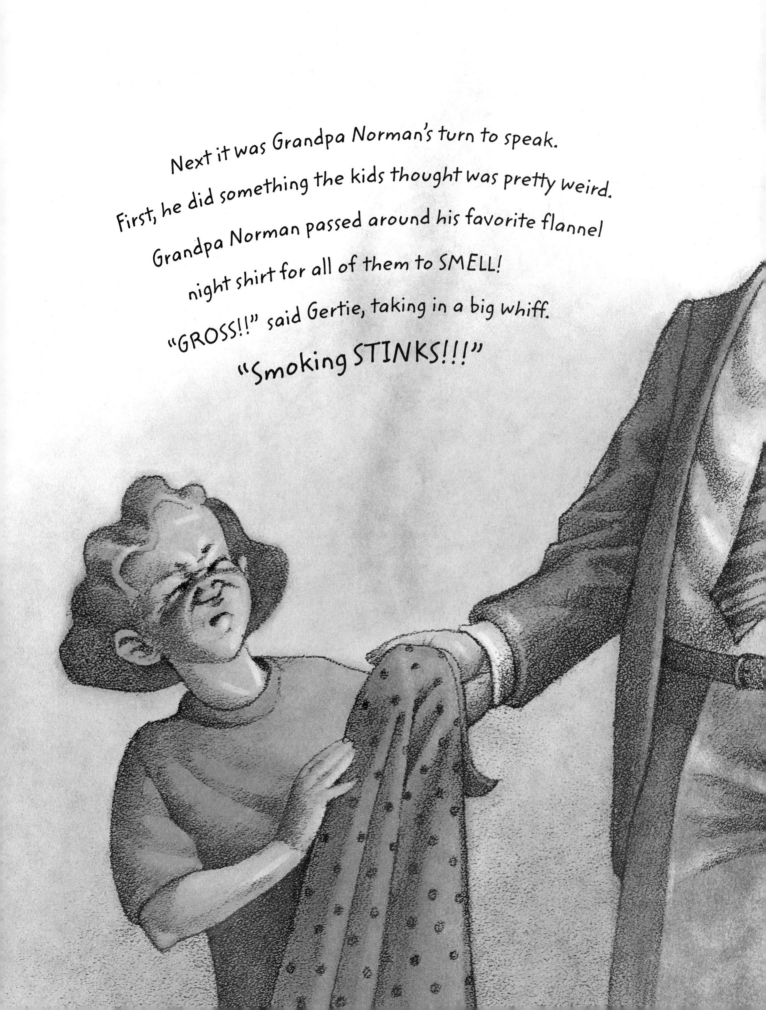

Grandpa Norman nodded, and went on to tell the kids about his experiences with smoking. "When I was a teenager," he said, "nobody seemed to know how bad smoking was. Now, we all know differently!"

"There's **NOTHING** good about smoking," Grandpa Norman said, sitting down to catch his breath.

Grandpa Norman told the class that sometimes (with a lot of help from their doctor, family and friends), people WERE able to quit smoking.

"It takes a lot of courage, and support," Grandpa Norman said, glancing at Dr. Parkin and Maddie.

"As of today, I've smoked my last cigarette!"

"Smoking's not as awesome as some of those older kids think!" Alex shouted defiantly. "Smoking STINKS!!" blurted out Maddie, in her loudest, biggest voice ever! This time, nobody giggled. Instead, the whole class stood up and cheered.

"Smoking STINKS!!"
...they all yelled together.... even Mr. Jenkins!

The End

Additional Resources

The following professional organizations may help provide
additional education and support:

AMERICAN LUNG ASSOCIATION

1740 Broadway
New York, NY 10019
(800)-LUNG-USA

AMERICAN CANCER SOCIETY

1599 Clifton Road, N.E.
Atlanta, GA 30329
(800) ACS-2345

AMERICAN HEART ASSOCIATION

7272 Greenville Avenue
Dallas, TX 75231
(800) AHA-USA1

AMERICAN ACADEMY OF PEDIATRICS

141 NW Point Boulevard
Elk Grove Village, IL 60007
(847) 228-5005

AMERICAN ACADEMY OF ALLERGY, ASTHMA, & IMMUNOLOGY

611 East Wells Street
Milwaukee, WI 53202
(800) 822-2762

CAMPAIGN FOR TOBACCO-FREE KIDS

1707 L Street, NW, Suite 800
Washington, DC 20036
(202) 296-5469
(800) 284-KIDS
Website: http://www.tobaccofreekids.org

THE FOUNDATION FOR A SMOKEFREE AMERICA

Patrick Reynolds, Founder and President
505 S. Beverly Dr., Suite 1000
Beverly Hills, CA 90212
(310) 277-1111
Website: http://www.tobaccofree.org

*Patrick Reynolds, grandson of tobacco company founder RJ Reynolds,
is a nationally known tobacco-free advocate. Call or visit their website to find
out how you can organize talks for Mr. Reynolds to elementary and high schools to
bring the smoke-free message to your community.*